Scales and Arpeggios for Guitar

Grades 1-5

The practice of scales and arpeggios plays an important part in the development of both technique and musicianship. Technically, scales and arpeggios encapsulate the very essence of guitar playing as they demand the exact co-ordination of both hands – holding down a note with the fingers of one hand and sounding it with the other. This technical matter can be smudged in the performance of pieces but is highlighted very clearly when playing scales and arpeggios.

Musically, scales and arpeggios provide the basic building blocks of so much music, and diligent study of their structure, fingerings and key zones in terms of the fingerboard is very important for musical development, particularly for skills such as sight-reading.

This manual does not offer detailed advice on the practice of technical requirements. All good teachers will have their own structured approaches to fingerings and there will be alternatives to those given here. (Some alternatives are provided to meet the needs of individual students and their adoption will depend on age, hand size and teaching plans.) It should be noted, however, that in the early grades there is a systematic exploration of certain positions and these positions should ideally be followed.

The Associated Board of
the Royal Schools of Music

Notes on the requirements

Reference must always be made to the syllabus for the year in which the examination is to be taken, in case any changes have been made to the requirements.

In the examination all scales and arpeggios must be played from memory.

Technical requirements should be played at a tempo which is consistent with accuracy, clarity, maximum legato and without undue accentuation. Recommended minimum speeds for the playing of scales are about ♪ = 88 at Grade 1, increasing to about ♪ = 184 by Grade 4 and reaching about ♩ = 120 by Grade 5.

A firm sonorous tone is expected, and for this reason the use of 'apoyando' strokes, though not obligatory, is recommended for the scales, whilst 'tirando' strokes should normally be used for playing all arpeggios, using the right-hand fingering pattern p.i.m.a.m.i.p. as a basis.

Right-hand fingerings for scales only will be specified by the examiner according to the requirements of the syllabus.

Contents

Grade 1

Major scales
with right-hand fingering i.m.

 **C MAJOR** 1 Octave

F MAJOR 1 Octave

G MAJOR 1 Octave

Minor scales
harmonic form *only*, with right-hand fingering i.m.

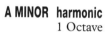 **A MINOR harmonic** 1 Octave

D MINOR harmonic 1 Octave

Chromatic scale
with right-hand fingering i.m.

 on G 1 Octave

Major arpeggios

C MAJOR 1 Octave

G MAJOR 1 Octave

Minor arpeggios

A MINOR 1 Octave

D MINOR 1 Octave

Grade 2

Major scales
with right-hand fingering i.m.

C MAJOR 1 Octave

D MAJOR 1 Octave
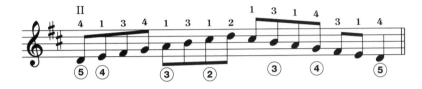

F MAJOR 1 Octave

G MAJOR 2 Octaves

Minor scales
B minor (harmonic form *only*) and D minor (melodic *or* harmonic form at candidate's choice), with right-hand fingering i.m.

B MINOR harmonic
1 Octave

D MINOR melodic
1 Octave

or

D MINOR harmonic
1 Octave

Chromatic scale
with right-hand fingering i.m.

on E 2 Octaves

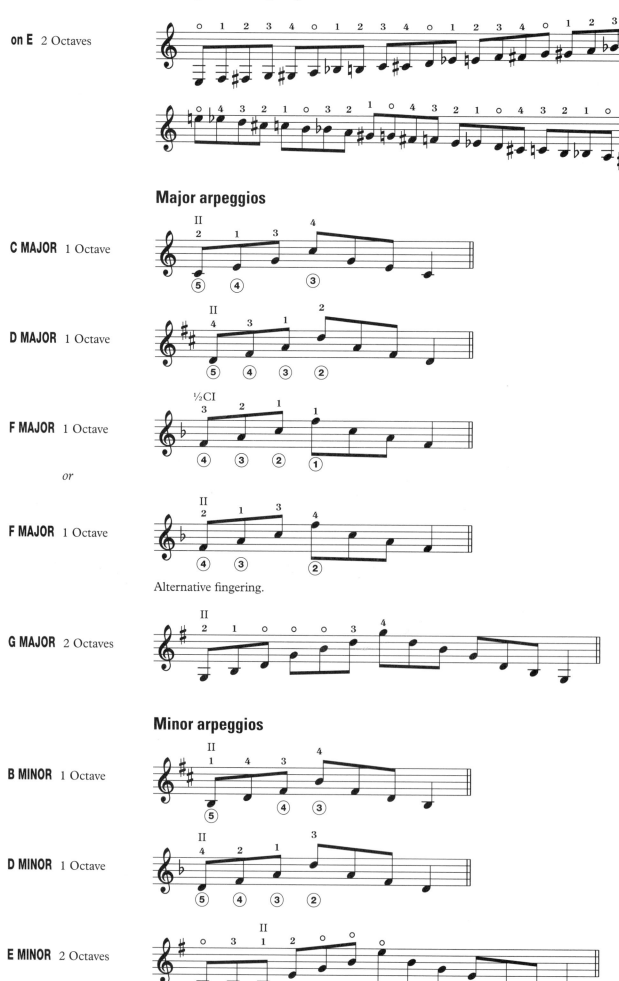

Major arpeggios

C MAJOR 1 Octave

D MAJOR 1 Octave

F MAJOR 1 Octave

or

F MAJOR 1 Octave

Alternative fingering.

G MAJOR 2 Octaves

Minor arpeggios

B MINOR 1 Octave

D MINOR 1 Octave

E MINOR 2 Octaves

6

Grade 3

Alternate fingers!

Major scales

with right-hand fingering i.m. *and* m.a.

D MAJOR 1 Octave

E MAJOR 1 Octave

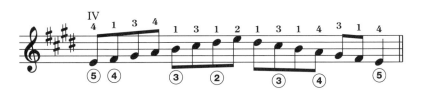

A MAJOR 2 Octaves

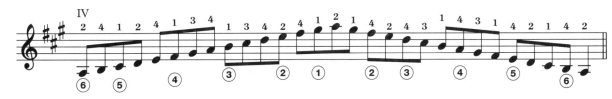

C MAJOR 2 Octaves

or

C MAJOR 2 Octaves

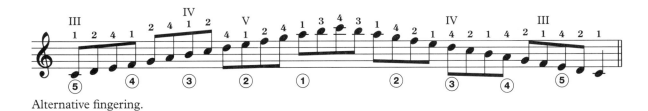

Alternative fingering.

Minor scales

C and C♯ minor (harmonic form *only*) and E minor (melodic *or* harmonic form at candidate's choice), with right-hand fingering i.m. *and* m.a.

C MINOR harmonic
2 Octaves

20/3/06

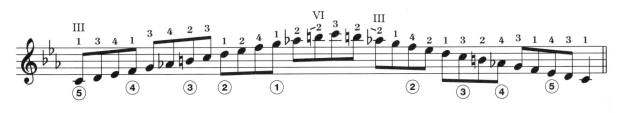

C♯ MINOR harmonic
1 Octave

20/3/06

E MINOR melodic
1 Octave

or

E MINOR harmonic
1 Octave

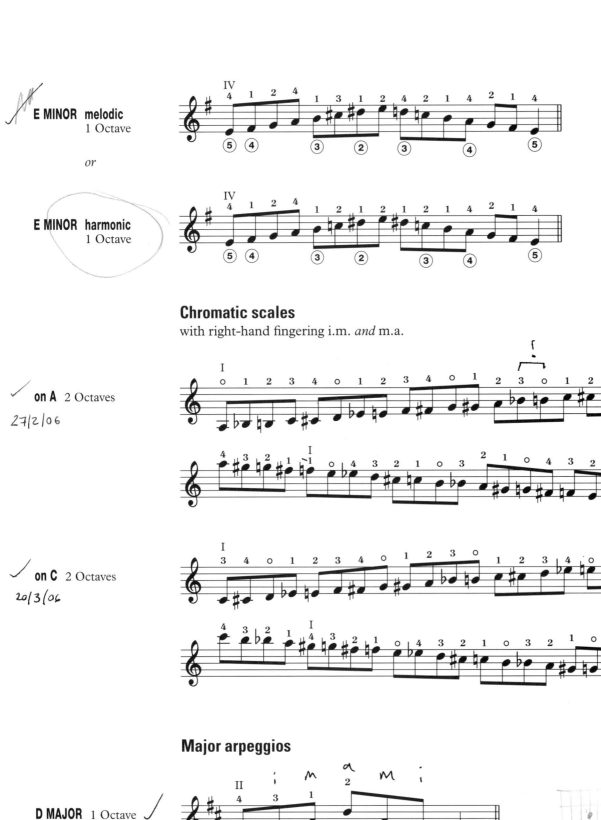

Chromatic scales

with right-hand fingering i.m. *and* m.a.

on A 2 Octaves
27/2/06

on C 2 Octaves
20/3/06

Major arpeggios

D MAJOR 1 Octave
20/3/06

or

~~**D MAJOR** 1 Octave~~

Alternative fingering.

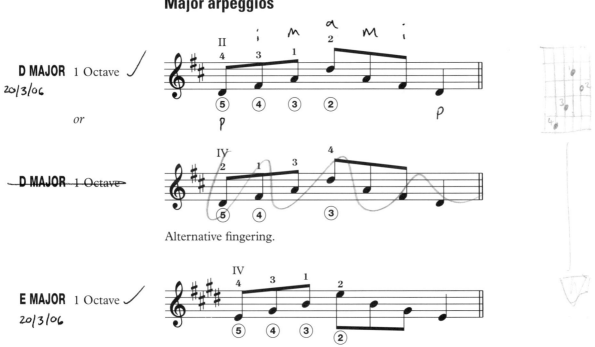

E MAJOR 1 Octave
20/3/06

AB 2563

A MAJOR 2 Octaves ✓

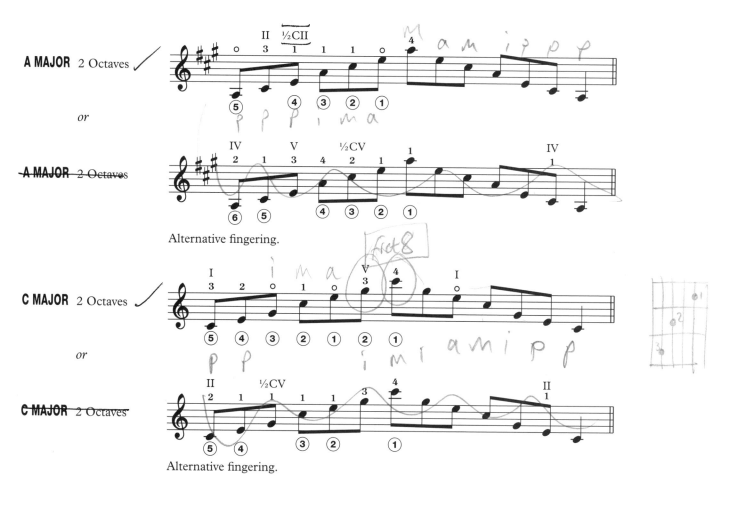

or

~~A MAJOR~~ ~~2 Octaves~~

Alternative fingering.

C MAJOR 2 Octaves ✓

or

~~C MAJOR~~ ~~2 Octaves~~

Alternative fingering.

Minor arpeggios

C# MINOR 1 Octave

E MINOR 1 Octave

Dominant sevenths

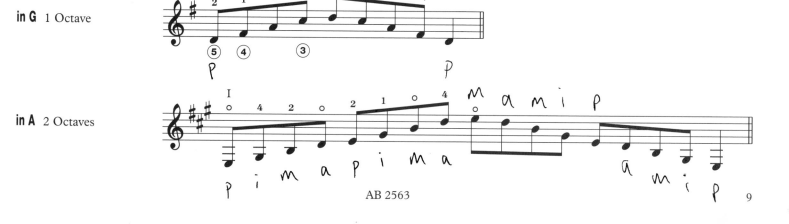

in G 1 Octave

in A 2 Octaves

AB 2563

9

Grade 4

Major scales

with right-hand fingering i.m. *and* m.a.

A MAJOR 2 Octaves

B♭ MAJOR 2 Octaves

C MAJOR 2 Octaves

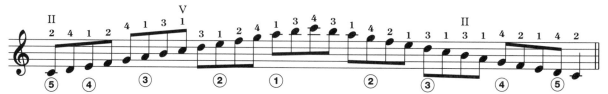

See p. 7 for alternative fingering.

D MAJOR 2 Octaves

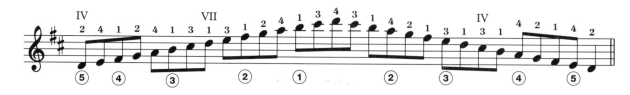

or

D MAJOR 2 Octaves

Alternative fingering.

Minor scales

melodic *or* harmonic form at candidate's choice, with right-hand fingering i.m. *and* m.a.

G MINOR melodic
2 Octaves

or

G MINOR harmonic
2 Octaves

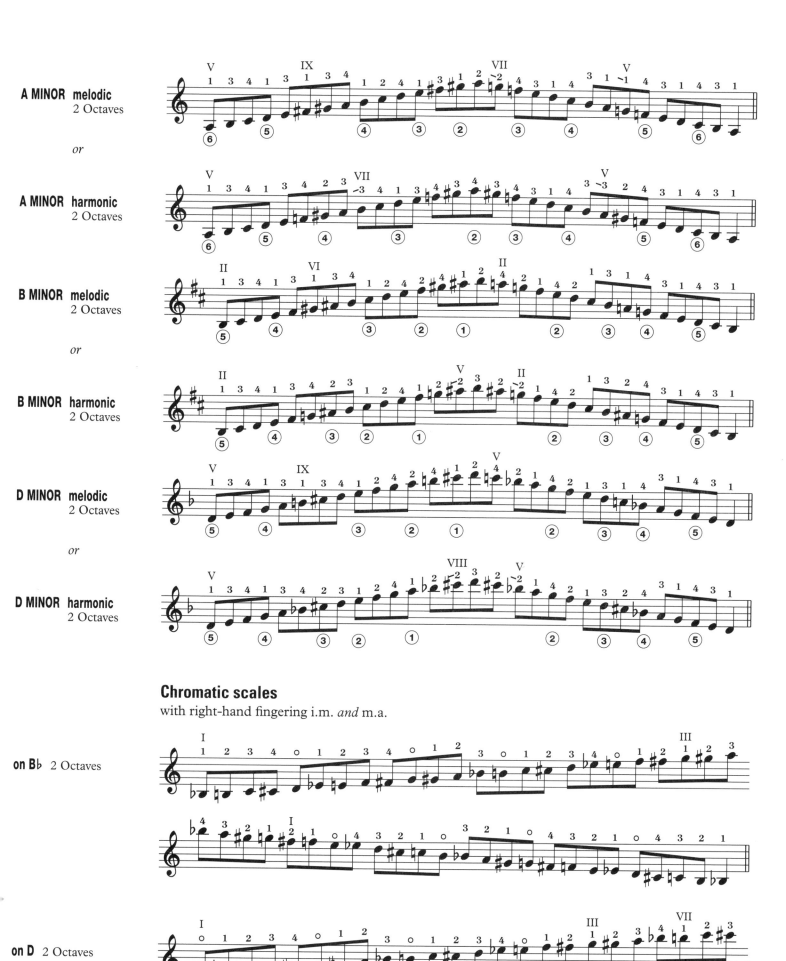

A MINOR melodic
2 Octaves

or

A MINOR harmonic
2 Octaves

B MINOR melodic
2 Octaves

or

B MINOR harmonic
2 Octaves

D MINOR melodic
2 Octaves

or

D MINOR harmonic
2 Octaves

Chromatic scales
with right-hand fingering i.m. *and* m.a.

on B♭ 2 Octaves

on D 2 Octaves

Major arpeggios

A MAJOR 2 Octaves

B♭ MAJOR 2 Octaves

C MAJOR 2 Octaves

See p. 9 for alternative fingerings.

D MAJOR 2 Octaves

or

D MAJOR 2 Octaves

Alternative fingering.

Minor arpeggios

G MINOR 2 Octaves

A MINOR 2 Octaves

B MINOR 2 Octaves

D MINOR 2 Octaves

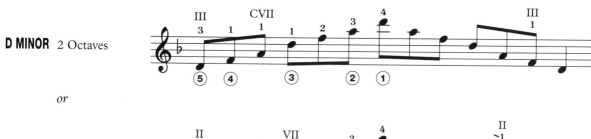

or

D MINOR 2 Octaves

Alternative fingering.

Dominant sevenths

in D 2 Octaves

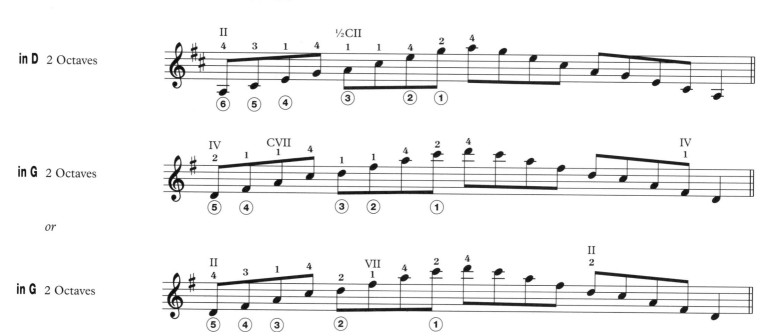

in G 2 Octaves

or

in G 2 Octaves

Alternative fingering.

Grade 5

Major scales

with right-hand fingering i.m. *and* m.a.

C MAJOR 2 Octaves

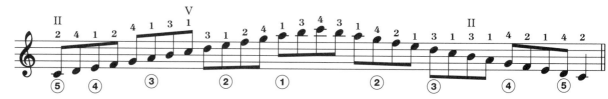

See p. 7 for alternative fingering.

Db MAJOR 2 Octaves

or

Db MAJOR 2 Octaves

Alternative fingering.

D MAJOR 2 Octaves

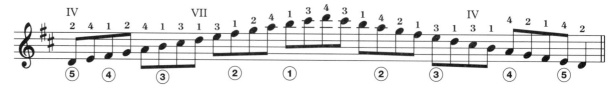

See p. 10 for alternative fingering.

Eb MAJOR 2 Octaves

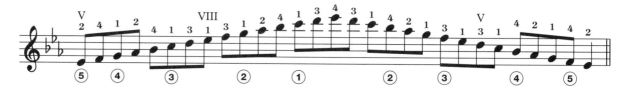

or

Eb MAJOR 2 Octaves

Alternative fingering.

E MAJOR 3 Octaves

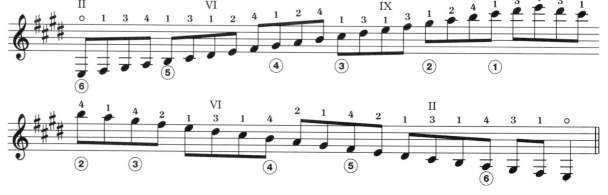

AB 2563

Minor scales

melodic *or* harmonic form at candidate's choice, with right-hand fingering i.m. *and* m.a.

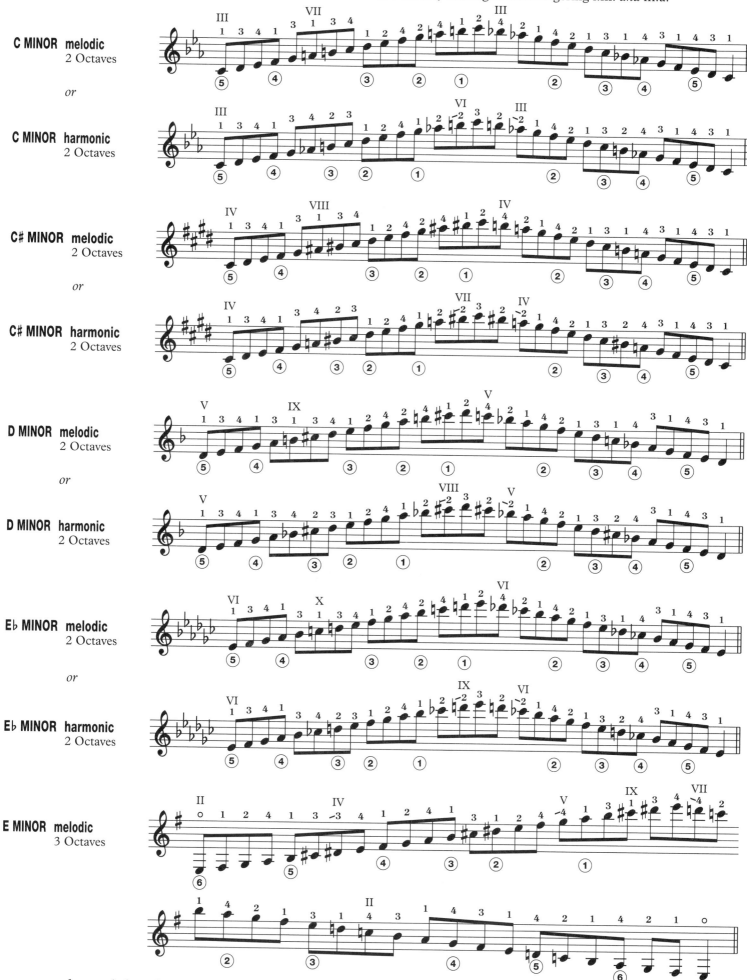

C MINOR melodic
2 Octaves

or

C MINOR harmonic
2 Octaves

C♯ MINOR melodic
2 Octaves

or

C♯ MINOR harmonic
2 Octaves

D MINOR melodic
2 Octaves

or

D MINOR harmonic
2 Octaves

E♭ MINOR melodic
2 Octaves

or

E♭ MINOR harmonic
2 Octaves

E MINOR melodic
3 Octaves

or harmonic form (see next page)

E MINOR harmonic
3 Octaves

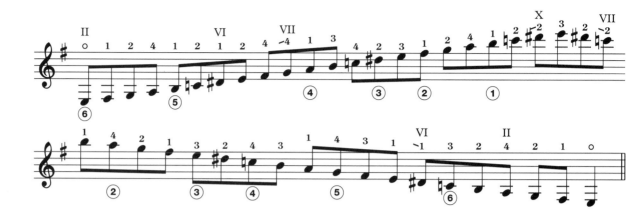

Chromatic scales

with right-hand fingering i.m. *and* m.a.

on C 2 Octaves

on C# 2 Octaves

on D 2 Octaves

on E♭ 2 Octaves

AB 2563

on E 3 Octaves

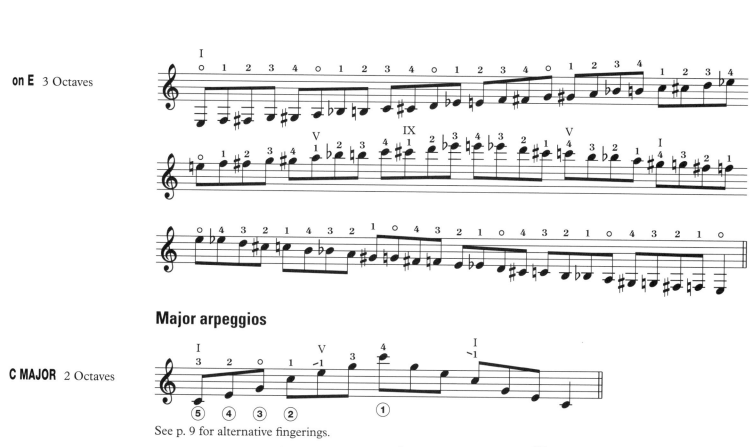

Major arpeggios

C MAJOR 2 Octaves

See p. 9 for alternative fingerings.

Db MAJOR 2 Octaves

or

Db MAJOR 2 Octaves

Alternative fingering.

D MAJOR 2 Octaves

See p. 12 for alternative fingering.

Eb MAJOR 2 Octaves

or

Eb MAJOR 2 Octaves

Alternative fingering.

E MAJOR 3 Octaves

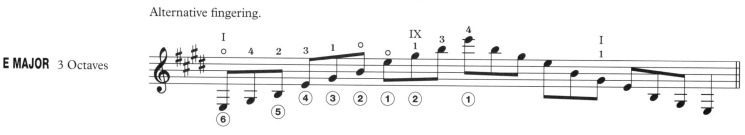

Minor arpeggios

C MINOR 2 Octaves

C# MINOR 2 Octaves

D MINOR 2 Octaves

See p. 13 for alternative fingering.

E♭ MINOR 2 Octaves

E MINOR 3 Octaves

Dominant sevenths

in F 2 Octaves

in F# 2 Octaves

in G 2 Octaves

or

in G 2 Octaves

Alternative fingering.

in A♭ 2 Octaves

or

in A♭ 2 Octaves

Alternative fingering.

Diminished sevenths

on C 2 Octaves

on D 2 Octaves

Double-stop scales

C MAJOR in thirds
1 Octave

C MAJOR in octaves
1 Octave

Music and text origination by
Barnes Music Engraving Ltd, East Sussex
Printed by Halstan & Co. Ltd., Amersham, Bucks., England